It is time to sing.

The mermaids are ready.
King Triton is ready.

But where is Ariel?

Ariel is in an old boat.

What is this?
Is it a human thing?

... OOPS! It is time to sing!

Ariel's father is angry.
"You are late for singing!
Stop playing with human things!
You are a mermaid!" Triton says.

Ariel loves human things.

This is her secret place.
Look at all the human things.

Look up! What is that?

Ariel swims to the top of the water.
She sees a big boat.
She swims toward it.

Ariel sees Prince Eric.

One, two legs.
She sees a dog.
One, two, three, four legs.

Ariel has no legs.

Listen. It is windy.
Look at the dark clouds.
Oh, no! It is a storm.

Prince Eric falls in the water.
Ariel swims fast.
She holds Prince Eric.
She swims up.

Ariel takes Prince Eric to the beach.
She looks at his face.
Is he sleeping?
Is he okay?

Prince Eric opens his eyes.
He is okay!

Ariel leaves the beach.

But she watches Prince Eric.

Ariels swims away.
She swims back to her home in the ocean.
But she thinks about Eric.

Ariel thinks and thinks.
Prince Eric, Prince Eric, Prince Eric,
Prince Eric!

Ariel loves Prince Eric.

"I love Prince Eric," Ariel says.
King Triton is angry.
"NO! You are a mermaid.
You're not human!"

"I'm not human *now*," Ariel says.
"But one day ... ."
Ariel leaves her father.
She swims toward Prince Eric.

Activities

Before You Read

1 **What lives in the ocean? Check (✓) the right pictures.**

| 4 | 1 | 2 | 3 | |

After You Read

1 **Read and answer Yes (Y) or No (N).**

- ☒ Ariel is human.
- ☑ Ariel loves Prince Eric.
- ☒ Triton is Ariel's brother.
- ☒ Prince Eric is a mermaid.
- ☑ Ariel lives in the ocean.

2 **What happens next? Check (✓) the right answers.**

- ☐ Ariel sings for Triton.
- ☐ Ariel lives with Prince Eric as a pet mermaid.
- ☑ Ariel grows legs and finds Prince Eric.
- ☑ Prince Eric lives in the ocean with Ariel.
- ☑ Ariel meets a nice fish.

Pearson Education Limited

Edinburgh Gate, Harlow,

Essex CM20 2JE, England

and Associated Companies throughout the world.

ISBN: 978-1-4082-8817-7

This edition first published by Pearson Education Ltd 2012

5 7 9 10 8 6 4

Set in 19/23pt OT Fiendstar Semibold

Printed in China

SWTC/04

Published by Pearson Education Ltd in association with
Penguin Books Ltd, both companies being subsidiaries of Pearson Plc

For a complete list of the titles available in the Penguin Kids series please go to www.penguinreaders.com.
Alternatively, write to your local Pearson Longman office or to: Penguin Readers Marketing Department,
Pearson Education, Edinburgh Gate, Harlow, Essex CM20 2JE, England.